MUSIC FOR SOLO FLUTE

EDITED BY TREVOR WYE

NOVELLO

SONATA IN A MINOR

C. PH. EMANUEL BACH
(1714-1788)

1

2

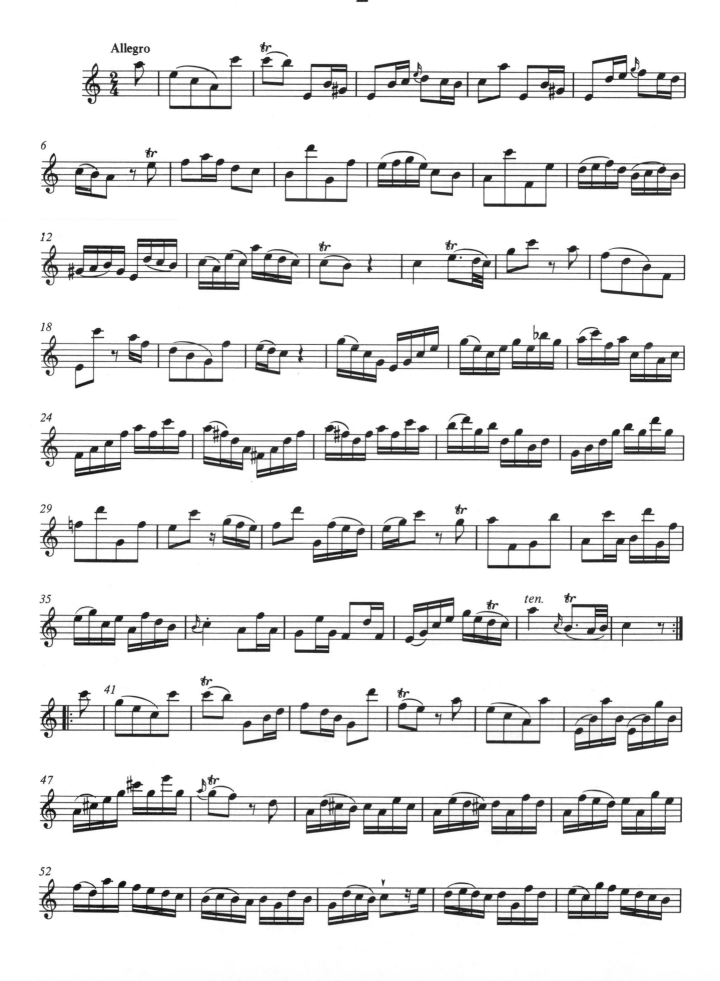

3

PARTITA IN A MINOR, BWV 1013

JOHANN SEBASTIAN BACH
(1685-1750)

8

N.B. There are no slurs in this movement in the original.

*Some believe this to be an F♯.

*Some believe this to be a B♮.

N.B. With the exception of the first, tenth and sixteenth bars all slurs are editorial.

12

Sarabande

*Probably an error.
  This bar should read:

N.B. There are no slurs in the original.

Bourrée Anglaise

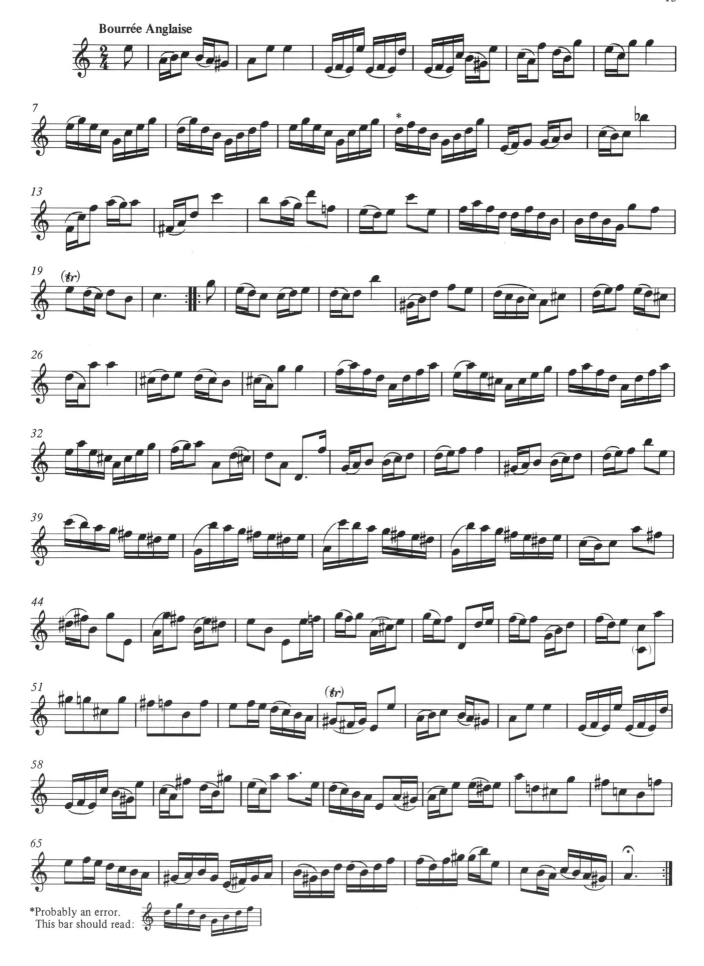

*Probably an error.
 This bar should read:

SONATA IN C MAJOR BWV 1033

JOHANN SEBASTIAN BACH
(1685-1750)

Allegro

*Probably an error.
This bar should read:

16

Adagio

5

8

11

Minuet I

6

11

da capo only

Minuet II

7

14

21

Minuet I da capo

SYRINX
for Solo Flute

CLAUDE DEBUSSY

*Debussy preferred it without this breath.

FANTASIE NO 2 IN A MINOR

TELEMANN

FANTASIE NO 3 IN B MINOR

TELEMANN

FANTASIE NO 4 IN B♭

TELEMANN

23

FANTASIE NO 6 IN D MINOR

TELEMANN

FANTASIE NO 7 IN D

TELEMANN

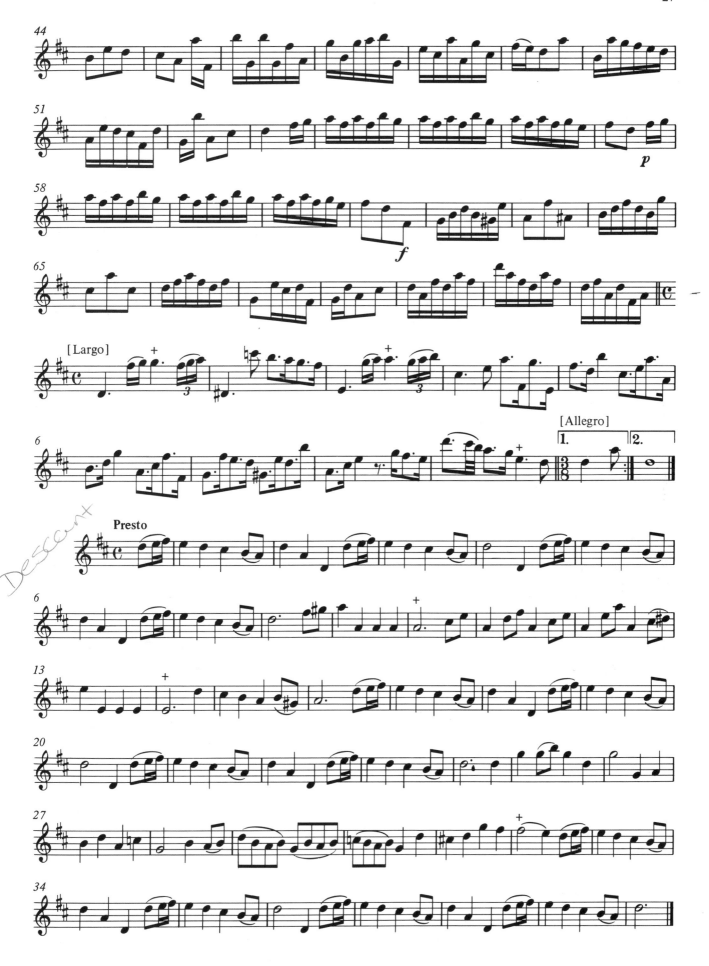

FANTASIE NO 10 IN F♯ MINOR

TELEMANN

FANTASIE NO 11 IN G

TELEMANN

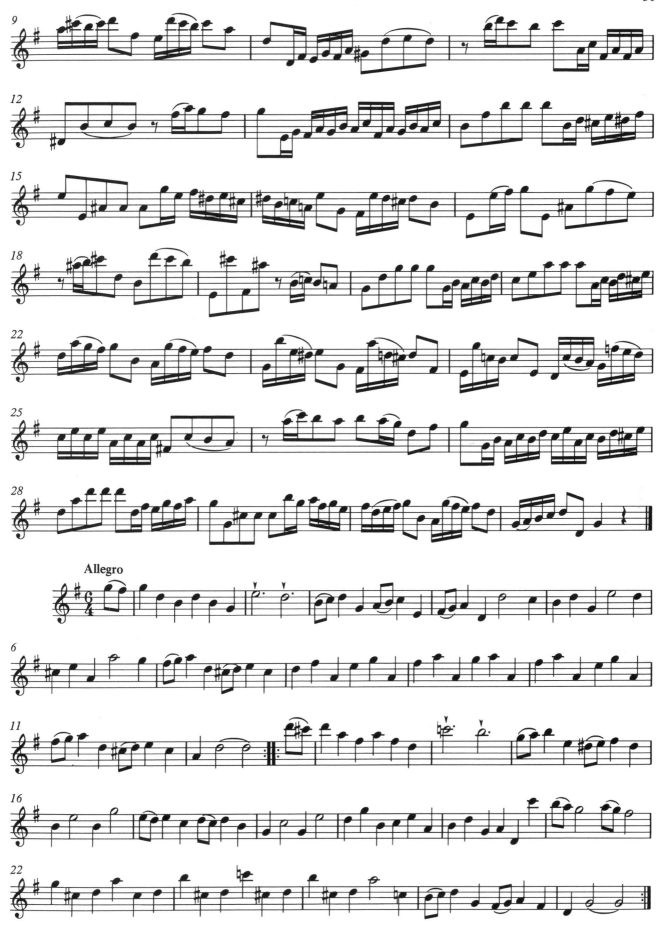

Printed and bound in Great Britain by
Caligraving Limited Thetford Norfolk

5/05 (54938)

CONTENTS